# Silas Greenshield's Guide

Charlotte Guillain
Illustrations by Dominik Domitrov

## Contents

OXFORD
UNIVERSITY PRESS

# Beast Hunter Beware!

Are you ready to seek out the world's most wild and dangerous creatures? Could *you* become the next Beast Hunter?

My name is Silas Greenshield. I am the last in the line of great beast hunters. I was born into a famous beast-hunting family. I have spent my life tracking down **terrifying** beasts and **gruesome** monsters that many people believe are just myths. I have been taught to defend myself against all types of creature and everything I have learned is recorded in these pages.

I hope that this book will help new beast hunters to continue my work. Read on and prepare to face the worst. First, you will need to put together a beast-hunting kit, though.

Silas Greenshield

Great-grandfather Aldous Greenshield

Aunt Greta Greenshield

Aunt Isadora Greenshield

Cousin Theodore Greenshield

## Beast-hunting Kit

You will need:

- honey to distract sweet-toothed beasts
- gold to buy safe **passage** from treasure-loving creatures
- a torch to distract fire-fearing beasts
- a thick cloak for warmth, protection and **camouflage**
- a violin for controlling elves
- a fireproof shield
- a mirror
- a tennis racket
- night-vision goggles
- a chain-mail vest for protection from deadly tickling (it's no laughing matter!)
- an invisibility potion to get out of tricky situations (watch out for my special recipe)
- this book!

## Danger rating

When you're hunting beasts, time is not always on your side. I've made this handy key so you can see at a glance how much trouble you're in!

*This beast may help you.*

*Dangerous beast: AVOID!*

*This beast will attack if provoked.*

*Deadly beast: RUN!*

# Trolls

These huge, **lumbering** brutes are not clever or cunning but they're very strong! You are most likely to find them after dark. During the day, they like to **lurk** in caves – so you should find other places to shelter!

poor eyesight

strong muscles

large, lumpy nose

dirty appearance

Trolls are large, slow and very ugly.

**Did you know?** Trolls have poor eyesight and are not very clever.

## Troll country

The best places to hunt for trolls are wild and mountainous areas in the northern countries of Scandinavia. However, recently they have been seen further south. Always stay alert when you travel through mountains and wild, rocky landscapes.

# Warning!

Trolls live in groups, so if you see one, watch out for others! Angry trolls can cause earthquakes and landslides by stamping their feet. They can also hurl large rocks. They usually eat sheep, goats and fish, but watch out for really hungry trolls. There's no telling what they might eat!

These strange rocks in the Norwegian mountains were once trolls. A clever beast hunter tricked them into watching the sunrise.

## Beating the beast!

Trolls are easily fooled – trick them and run away! They are scared of lightning and other sudden flashes of light. Finally, and most importantly, remember that trolls are turned to stone by sunlight.

*Dangerous beast: AVOID!*

# Krakens

All sorts of terrible monsters lurk in the deepest parts of the oceans. The kraken is the most dangerous of all. This gigantic, squid-like creature can grow up to 15 metres long and terrorizes sailors in northern seas. Watch out for huge, slimy tentacles creeping on to your ship's deck.

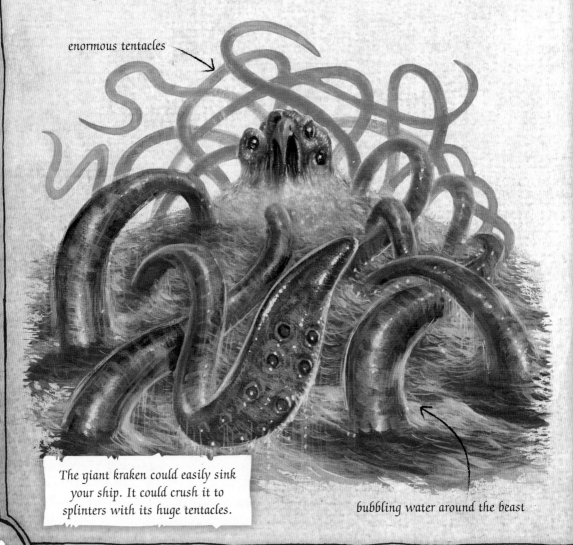

enormous tentacles

The giant kraken could easily sink your ship. It could crush it to splinters with its huge tentacles.

bubbling water around the beast

# Kraken attack!

A fisherman in the Arctic Ocean slipped this message into a bottle. The bottle made it back to shore but the fisherman has not been heard of since.

Our fishing boat arrived at a small island. We dropped anchor and rowed ashore in a small boat. The island's surface was slimy but we thought it must be a strange seaweed. Suddenly, the 'ground' beneath us began to shudder. This was no island – it was a kraken's back! Long tentacles slid out of the sea and gripped our fishing boat. There was a rush of water as the huge monster rose up, throwing us into the water. We clambered into the rowing boat as the kraken thrashed around. Suddenly, it disappeared below the surface, taking our fishing boat with it. Now we are adrift at sea. SOS!

## 𝓑eating the beast!

The kraken won't attack unless it is disturbed. Avoid fishing or lowering an anchor away from the shore, unless you want to stir the beast in the shadowy depths.

*This beast will attack if provoked.*

# Dragons

Only the bravest beast hunter goes looking for dragons. They live all over the world and usually make their dens on top of **fiery** volcanoes as these are the best places to hoard treasure – especially gold!

sharp spines along back

large, leathery wings

razor-sharp teeth

breathes fire

deadly talons

scaly skin

The European dragon can grow up to 21 metres long from snout to tail.

# Watch the skies!

Dragons can breathe fire over several metres so it's important to keep your distance. Always be on your guard as dragons can swoop down and surprise even experienced beast hunters, attacking them with their sharp teeth and claws. Finally, remember dragons will attack *anyone* who goes near their hoard of gold.

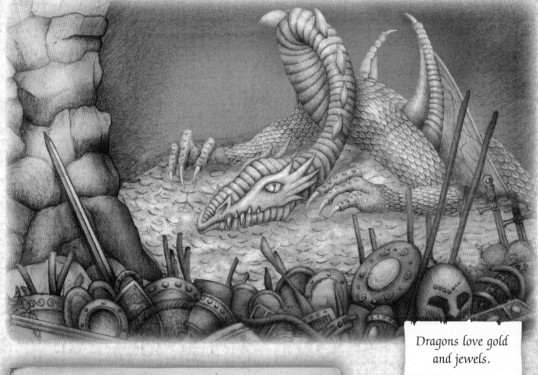

Dragons love gold and jewels.

### Beating the beast!

A dragon's enormous size is terrifying but you can use it to your advantage. Hide in a small cave or **crevice** where the beast can't see you.

**Deadly beast: RUN!**

# Boggarts

Boggarts are powerful and mean. They are also what's known as shape-shifters. This means they can change the way they look. It's said that they often take the shape of a person's worst fear.

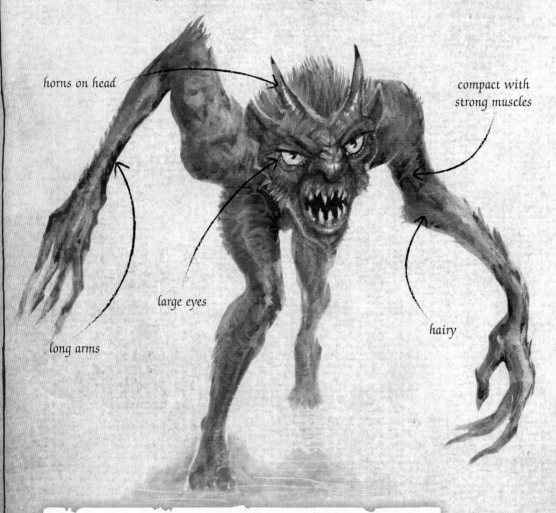

horns on head

compact with strong muscles

long arms

large eyes

hairy

Beast hunters can spot boggarts who have changed shape by looking out for the horns on their heads. These don't go when they change shape.

# Boggart battle

My great-grandfather, the famous beast hunter Aldous Greenshield, wrote about his encounter with a boggart.

**Top tip!**
Never travel without a pot of honey. Boggarts have a sweet tooth and won't be able to resist it!

## 15th November, 1899

A boggart had **invaded** a farmer's cottage and was smashing plates, breaking furniture and terrifying visitors. I armed myself with a wild honeycomb (stolen from the local beehives) and a mirror, and entered the dark cottage. The beast was hiding in the shadows so I placed the honeycomb on the floor. The boggart shuffled out and began lapping up the honey. I edged towards it but it **lashed out** with its deadly long arms. It threw me across the room but I staggered back towards it. As the boggart jumped up to attack, I held the mirror over my face. The boggart saw its own reflection and vanished.

## Beating the beast!

Don't try to fight a boggart with weapons. Its strength and speed will always overpower you. A mirror is your best defence – a boggart is destroyed if it sees its own **hideous** reflection.

*Dangerous beast: AVOID!*

# Elves

Don't believe the stories you've heard about sweet and kind elves – most of them are incredibly nasty! Elves that live underground are *especially* dangerous. They love to trick humans. They may even try to turn you against your fellow travellers!

grey, scaly skin

long, crooked nose

claw-like fingers

fang-like teeth

If they touch humans, elves can cause a horribly painful illness. This is known as 'elf-shot'.

**Did you know?**
It's best to stay awake when travelling in elf country. Elves can turn your dreams into terrifying nightmares!

# Recent sightings

The most recent elf sightings have been in Central and Eastern Europe. Beast hunters believe they are moving further east. Elves live in caves, forests and underground burrows. They ambush unsuspecting travellers and steal their precious items. They can cause mayhem. They often creep into human homes at night to cause trouble.

## Basic elvish

These phrases might be useful if you meet elves:

Good evening.
*Akreech burgwix.*

Stay away from me.
*Nopcrew ba sneep higg.*

I've got a violin in my bag.
*Julla sqeewee neish
div snaw-thak.*

Elves ambush travellers by leaping out of underground burrows.

## Beating the beast!

Always carry a violin with you as elves hate music, particularly when played on a violin. Play for just a few minutes and the elf will be on its knees, begging you to stop.

*Dangerous beast:
AVOID!*

# Griffins

These powerful beasts have the body of a lion and head of an eagle. Most griffins live in southern Europe, the Middle East and North Africa. Griffins are unusual. They are angry if provoked but if you approach with care, a griffin could offer you help.

strong, sharp beak

head and wings of an eagle

eagle's talons

body, legs and tail of a lion

Griffins are often thought of as the king of all creatures. They are a combination of the lion (the king of beasts) and the eagle (the king of birds).

# Griffin gifts

Griffins often help humans that they trust. They have given beast hunters many gifts over the years.

## Greenshield family guide to the power of griffin gifts

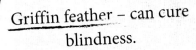

Griffin feather – can cure blindness.

Griffin claw – can be ground into a powder and used to cure illness and heal injuries.

Griffin gold – has magical properties and can be used many times.

### Beating the beast!

If you find yourself nose to beak with an angry griffin, watch out for the tail. It can whip round and knock you off your feet in a flash.

*This beast may help you.*

# Chonchons

If you go beast hunting in South America, you may **encounter** a chonchon. These creatures have a body shaped like a human head with massive ears. They use these as wings! Chonchons also have feathers and sharp claws. Chonchons fly around at night, looking for victims to bite so they can drink their blood.

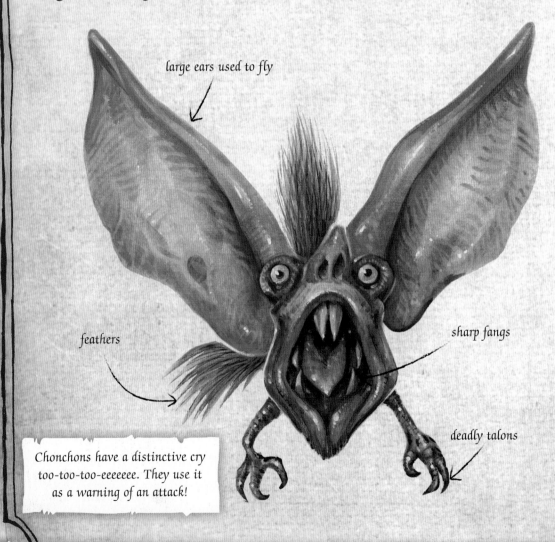

large ears used to fly

feathers

sharp fangs

deadly talons

Chonchons have a distinctive cry too-too-too-eeeeeee. They use it as a warning of an attack!

# Eyewitness account

My Aunt Isadora met a chonchon on her travels through South America. She wrote to warn me about these fearsome beasts.

Dear Silas,

I have made it safely through Argentina and Chile but nearly met my end at the hands (or talons) of a chonchon! This creepy creature hunts on dark nights. It flaps silently through the sky with its huge, ridiculous ears. I was camping under the stars and was woken by its screech as it dived towards me. I whacked it with my umbrella before it could bite me. The chonchon was scared away but I didn't sleep again that night.

Always intrepid,

Aunt Isadora xx

## Did you know?

Chonchons have incredible night vision. Always carry night-vision goggles with you to help you see well in the dark and spot an attack!

## Beating the beast!

Chonchons are easily knocked off course and quickly become dizzy. My Aunt Isadora used an umbrella to bat one away but you could carry a tennis racquet for more power.

*Dangerous beast:*
*AVOID!*

# Goblins

These gruesome-looking creatures lurk in dark places looking for trouble. They take great pleasure in tricking or attacking travellers so they can steal their money. Goblins are very greedy.

**Did you know?**

Goblins are vicious fighters. They are famous for carrying deadly weapons. Avoid a fight – it's better to hide or run.

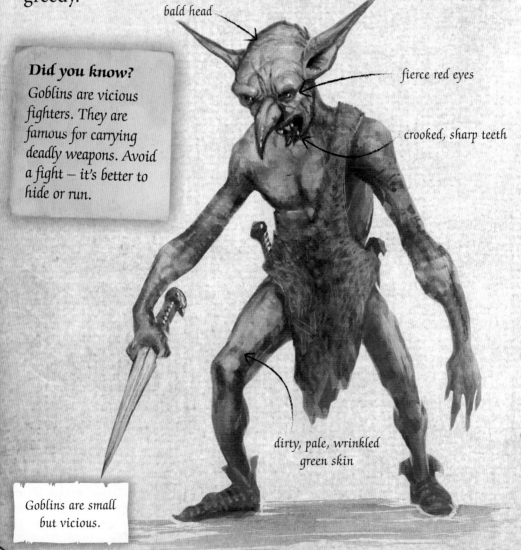

bald head

fierce red eyes

crooked, sharp teeth

dirty, pale, wrinkled green skin

Goblins are small but vicious.

# A traveller's tale

Famous beast hunter Bjørn encountered goblins on his travels. He told me the following tale.

In one of the deepest, darkest forests in Russia, I heard the sound of quarrelling ahead. I slipped behind a tree and peered from the shadows. Two goblins were fighting – biting and scratching each other. Before I could slip away, they stopped and sniffed the air. They had smelled me! Suddenly, they ran towards my hiding place, grinning evilly. I lit a dry branch, which I waved towards them and they backed away from the flames. Then I grabbed a handful of gold from my bag and threw it down. As they scrabbled and scrapped over the shiny coins, I ran away as fast as I could.

*Goblins take their victims by surprise.*

## $\mathcal{B}$eating the beast!

Goblins are afraid of fire. You can trick them if you carry a torch in your bag. Switch it on and shine it in their eyes. They will think it is fire and will run away.

*Deadly beast: RUN!*

# Bunyips

If you travel through Australia, watch out for bunyips. You will find them around water-holes. They never stray too far from water. These large, blubbery beasts are calm when swimming but can become very angry on land.

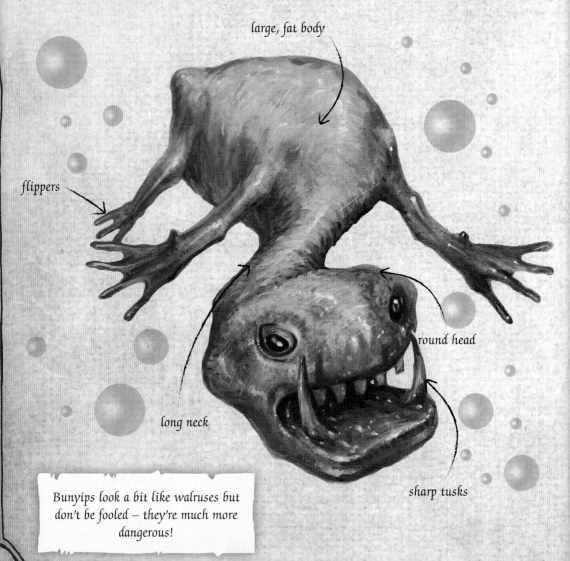

large, fat body

flippers

round head

long neck

sharp tusks

Bunyips look a bit like walruses but don't be fooled – they're much more dangerous!

# Danger down under

Listen out for a bellowing, booming roar near water-holes. This spine-chilling sound warns you that a bunyip is nearby. Bunyips usually eat small animals and fish but a hungry one could easily gobble down a human. Even if you manage to escape, an attack from their tusks would cause you serious harm!

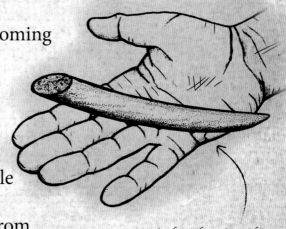

*A sharp bunyip tusk can grow to over 20 cm.*

## Beating the beast!

Follow these instructions if you meet an angry bunyip:

1. Stand still and make yourself look as big and tall as possible. If you're wearing a cloak, open it out out to make yourself look bigger.

2. Shout as loudly as you can. You might be able to scare the bunyip off.

3. If the bunyip runs at you, stay still as long as you dare and then jump to the side at the last moment.

4. If you have any food, throw it as far away as you can to distract the bunyip. Then run away!

**Did you know?**
Bunyips can run surprisingly fast. Don't get in their way as they will trample you!

**This beast will attack if provoked.**

# Ogres

If you saw a footprint like this, what would you do? Run? You'd be right. This footprint belongs to an ogre. These huge, muscle-bound thugs stomp around most of Europe, looking for good things to eat. If you come across one, don't let it think you're its next meal!

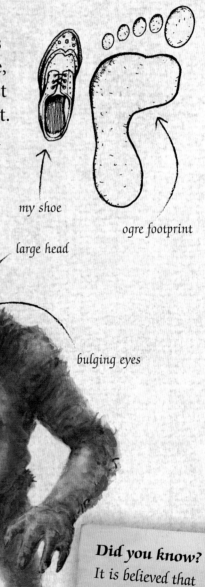

my shoe

ogre footprint

large head

bulging eyes

warty skin

Ogres are one of the largest and strongest beasts you will encounter.

round stomach

**Did you know?**
It is believed that 'ogre' is originally a French word.

## Textbook ogres

My cousin Theodore has written a book on ogres. It has lots of information about the history of ogres and how to avoid upsetting them!

### Beating the beast!

Ogres are lumbering and slow, so your best defence is simple – try to outrun them!

*Extract from:*

## The Odious History of Ogres
### by Professor Theodore Broadsword

The first ogres were seen in France during the 12th century. Shepherds came across them in lonely mountain caves. As the human population spread, ogres moved to live in even more remote places. By the 17th century, ogre sightings were made as far away as Russia and the Middle East.

Ogres only bother humans when:

- beast hunters or travellers cross their territory
- livestock herders are forced to take their flocks close to the beasts' caves
- they are hungry and **venture** into villages and towns looking for food.

## Tell-tale signs

Is it an ogre? Here are some tell-tale signs:

1. The smell! Ogres are horribly stinky so you can normally smell one before you see it.
2. Is it sniffing the air? Does it look hungry? Ogres are constantly looking for food.
3. Does it look grumpy? Ogres are very grumpy so don't risk annoying one!

*Dangerous beast: AVOID!*

# Abadas

Beast hunters travelling through Africa's deepest jungles may be lucky enough to come across an abada. Like the griffin, these beautiful beasts could help you. These shy, horse-like creatures have shiny, curved horns with special powers.

two curved horns

long, thick mane

long, curly tail

body like a small horse

The timid abada is about the size of a small donkey.

# Hidden helper

Jungle river water can make you sick if you drink it. However, if an abada's horn touches the water, it will become safe to drink. It will also cure illnesses and give you energy. If you treat an abada gently and respectfully, it will lead you safely through even the most dense forest.

## Magical relative

In other parts of the world you may come across the abada's relative, the unicorn.

Look out for these features:

- horse-like appearance
- single, spiralling horn
- silvery-white coat
- beard like a goat's.

Seeing a unicorn will bring a traveller good luck and special protection from more dangerous beasts.

The horn of a unicorn also has magical healing properties.

## Beating the beast!

Abadas will help you if they trust you. Try not to scare them away – be very quiet and don't make any sudden movements. If you are lucky enough to meet an abada, stay still until it comes to you.

*This beast may help you.*

# Leshis

If you head east through Europe, look out for leshis. These mischievous beasts love to get travellers lost. Their favourite method of attack is unusual. It might sound funny but it can be deadly! (See 'Beating the beast!')

branch-like limbs

green eyes

pale grey skin with patches of moss

Leshis are easy to miss because they blend in with the trees.

hooves like a goat

# Leshi lowdown

Leshis may look harmless but beware – they will call out and pretend to be human. This is to confuse you! They can **mimic** any voice to lure you into their caves. Then they attack by tickling. Many travellers have died laughing after just a few minutes of leshi tickling.

I have **witnessed** a leshi attack myself. This is a page from my Eastern European travel journal.

### 28th July

We have been travelling through a remote Bulgarian forest for days. We had seen no beasts until this morning. We stopped to swim in a stream, leaving our clothes on the bank. Suddenly, strange shrieks came from the trees. It sounded like our own voices calling out! Confused, we climbed out and began to get dressed.

Suddenly, a leshi jumped out and began tickling my old friend, Wilfred. Panicking, I grabbed my clothes and put them on inside out and back to front! When the leshi saw me, it howled and pointed at my clothes. Then it quickly scrambled away. We stayed dressed like this until we were safely out of the forest.

## $\mathcal{B}$eating the beast!

When travelling in leshi country, wear all your clothes inside out and back to front. Leshis find this so funny and confusing, they forget to attack!

*Dangerous beasts: AVOID!*

# Final words of warning

The world will always need beast hunters like you and me. Most people think beasts and monsters exist only in fairy tales, but we know the truth. Make sure you use your knowledge wisely.

As you travel the world, try to collect souvenirs from the beasts you meet. They can be used to make an invisibility potion – the best defence a beast hunter can have. This is my family recipe. Guard it with your life – it might just save yours.

## INVISIBILITY POTION

### Ingredients

1 litre of water cleaned by an abada's horns

3 dragon scales

1 scrape of slime from a kraken's tentacle

5 boggart hairs

1 spoonful of troll earwax

1 elf claw

2 griffin feathers

50 ml of chonchon tears

A pinch of dirt scraped from a goblin's fingernails

1 bunyip tooth

1 handful of moss from a leshi's arm

1 ogre nail

1 ogre sock

A handful of berries (to improve the taste)

# Instructions

1. Bring the water to the boil in a large pot.

2. Add the dragon scales one by one until they dissolve.

3. Stir as you add the kraken slime, boggart hairs and troll earwax. Leave to simmer.

4. Grate the elf claw finely (take care not to scratch yourself!). Add this and the griffin feathers to the pot. Stir for ten minutes.

5. Add the chonchon tears a drop at a time. Purple smoke will rise from the surface.

6. Bring to the boil. Stir in the goblin fingernail dirt, bunyip tooth and leshi moss. Leave to cook for around an hour with the lid on.

7. The mixture should be smooth and thick and a golden-red colour. Add a squeeze of sweat from the ogre sock and berries of your choice.

8. Pour the potion into a strong bottle and bury it underground until your next adventure.

# Test your knowledge

Before you hunt for mythical beasts, take this test.
Can you remember the deadly details? They could
save your life.

**1) What should you do if you come across trolls?**
   a. Draw your sword and attack.
   b. Start chatting and try to befriend them.
   c. Run away as fast as you can.

**2) How big can a kraken grow?**
   a. 15 metres long
   b. Several miles long
   c. 100 metres long

**3) How can you recognize a boggart when
   it shape-shifts?**
   a. Look for its horns.
   b. Its voice stays the same.
   c. It always smells of swamp gas.

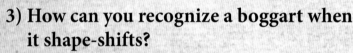

**4) Where do most elves live?**
   a. In underground burrows.
   b. On top of volcanoes.
   c. In dark corners of human houses.

**5) Which animals does a griffin resemble?**
   a. A wolf and an owl
   b. A dog and a deer
   c. A lion and an eagle

**6) How can you scare off goblins?**
   a.  By shouting very loudly.
   b.  By blowing a whistle.
   c.  With fire.

**7) Where in the world do bunyips live?**
   a.  Australia
   b.  New Zealand
   c.  Japan

**8) What's usually the first sign that an ogre is near?**
   a.  It likes to sing very badly.
   b.  Its disgusting smell.
   c.  The ground trembles under its feet.

**9) How can an abada help you?**
   a.  It will give you a ride on its back.
   b.  It will take you to fruit trees in the forest.
   c.  Its horn makes water safe to drink.

**10) How can a leshi harm travellers?**
   a.  It squashes them in a big hug.
   b.  It tickles them to death.
   c.  It bites them and drinks their blood.

If you score 6, go forth and track; below 6, learn
some more – it's not safe for you out there!

# Glossary

| | |
|---|---|
| **camouflage** | way of hiding something |
| **crevice** | narrow opening |
| **encounter** | meet unexpectedly |
| **fiery** | looking like fire or made of fire |
| **gruesome** | really horrible |
| **hideous** | very ugly or disgusting |
| **invaded** | entered without permission |
| **lashed out** | struck at |
| **lumbering** | moving very heavily |
| **lurk** | wait in a hidden or secret place |
| **mimic** | copy |
| **passage** | moving from one place to another |
| **terrifying** | very frightening |
| **venture** | go somewhere you don't know that might be dangerous |
| **witnessed** | saw something happening |

# Index